60 recipes from the best of Weight Watchers cookbooks
including over 20 vegetarian recipes, all low in *POINTS* values

just for me

SIMON &
SCHUSTER

First published in Great Britain
by Simon & Schuster UK Ltd, 2009
A CBS Company

Copyright © 2009 Weight Watchers International, Inc.

Simon & Schuster UK Ltd
1st Floor, 222 Gray's Inn Road,
London WC1X 8HB

1 3 5 7 9 10 8 6 4 2

The recipes in this book were created for Weight Watchers
by *Sue Ashworth, Sue Beveridge, Tamsin Burnett-Hall, Nicola
Graimes, Becky Johnson, Kim Morphew, Joy Skipper* and
Penny Stephens.

Weight Watchers Publications Team:
Jane Griffiths, Donna Watts and *Nina McKerlie*
Photography: *Steve Baxter, Steve Lee* and *Juliet Piddington*
Design and typesetting: *Fiona Andreanelli*

Printed and bound in Singapore

ISBN 978-1-84737-650-3
A CIP catalogue for this book is available from the British
Library

Pictured on the front cover: Sizzling steak stir fry, page 39
Pictured on the contents page: Cajun steak muffin, page 34
Pictured on the back cover: Parsnip cakes with poached
egg, page 16; Thai beef salad, page 29; Penne forestiere,
page 47.

**A selection of Online recipes and images
appear courtesy of weightwatchers.co.uk.**

POINTS® value logo: You'll find this easy to read
POINTS value logo on every recipe throughout
this book. The logo represents the number of **POINTS**
values per serving each recipe contains. Weight Watchers
POINTS system is a simple way to lose weight. As part of
the Weight Watchers Discover Plan™, you'll enjoy eating
delicious, healthy, filling foods that help keep you feeling
satisfied for longer and in control of both your portion sizes
and your hunger.

Filling Foods are highlighted in green – like this. Focus on
these foods where you can – they keep you feeling satisfied
for longer.

Y This symbol denotes a vegetarian recipe and
assumes that, where relevant, free range eggs, vegetarian
cheese, vegetarian virtually fat free fromage frais and
vegetarian low fat crème fraîche are used. Virtually fat free
fromage frais and low fat crème fraîche may contain traces
of gelatine so they are not always vegetarian. Please check
the labels.

✳ This symbol denotes a dish that can be frozen.

Recipe notes:
Egg size: Medium, unless otherwise stated.
All fruits and vegetables: Medium sized unless otherwise
stated.
Raw eggs: Only the freshest eggs should be used. Pregnant
women, the elderly and children should avoid recipes with
eggs that are not fully cooked or raw.
Recipe timings: These are approximate and meant to be
guidelines. Please note that the preparation time includes
all the steps up to and following the main cooking time(s).
Polyunsaturated margarine: Use brands such as Flora Light,
St Ivel Gold and Benecol Light.

Contents

Just for Me is a delicious and satisfying collection of 60 recipes taken from the best of Weight Watchers cookbooks, all just for one. This is the ideal cookbook whether you regularly cook only for yourself or for those occasions when you find you are the only one at home and you want to prepare something just for you. You'll no longer be tempted to have something less healthy.

You'll find a range of recipes that are certain to inspire you to cook – from breakfasts and brunches to lunches and dinners. And the majority of recipes are ready in 30 minutes or less and all can be made with the minimum of fuss.

Just for Me is perfect for everyone, including adult children who may be fleeing the nest for the first time or heading off to University. Whether they are looking to lose or maintain their weight or just enjoy healthy, delicious meals – they'll find lots to choose from.

All the recipes in *Just for Me* are easy to follow and full of healthy, nutritious ingredients that can help you stay satisfied for longer. Each recipe has a **POINTS** value clearly shown so you can easily track what you're eating and stay within your **POINTS** allowance. Use *Just for Me* alongside the Discover Plan to help your **POINTS** allowance go further, as many of the recipes contain **Filling Foods**.

A delicious and satisfying selection of recipes to get you off to a great start each morning and keep hunger at bay until lunchtime so you can avoid reaching for an unhealthy mid-morning snack.

Florentine mushrooms

A mouth watering vegetarian, cooked breakfast treat.

2 **POINTS** values per recipe • **162** Calories per serving • Takes 10 minutes • Ⓨ

2 large, flat mushrooms, stalks removed
low fat cooking spray
100 g (3½ oz) baby spinach leaves
1 tablespoon low fat soft cheese
1 egg
salt and freshly ground black pepper

❶ Preheat the grill to medium.
❷ Place the mushrooms in a baking dish, lightly spray with the cooking spray and season inside and out. Grill for 2 minutes, stalk side down, then turn over and grill for 2 minutes more, or until tender.
❸ Meanwhile, bring a pan of water to the boil for the poached egg and place the spinach in a separate lidded saucepan. Cover the spinach and cook over a low heat until wilted. Stir in the soft cheese and seasoning, then keep warm.
❹ Break the egg into a cup. Use a spoon to create a whirlpool effect in the pan of boiling water, then slip in the egg. Reduce the water to a gentle simmer and cook for 3–4 minutes or until the egg is cooked to your liking.
❺ To serve, nestle the mushrooms side by side on a warm plate, and spoon the creamy spinach on top. Lift the egg out of the pan using a slotted spoon and rest on top of the mushrooms. Serve immediately.

Zingy vegetable juice

This is a wonderful morning reviver packed with powerful nutrients and cleansing refreshment. For best results use a juicer, then you could use raw beetroot instead of cooked.

2½ **POINTS** values per recipe • **275** Calories per serving • Takes 5 minutes • **Y** Vegan

100 g (3½ oz) cooked beetroot (vacuum packed or freshly cooked and peeled), sliced
1 large carrot, sliced
4 cm (1½ inch) fresh root ginger, peeled and grated finely
2 apples, peeled, cored and chopped roughly
150 g (5½ oz) red or white seedless grapes

❶ Place all the ingredients in a food processor or blender and blend for a few minutes or until fairly smooth. Strain and serve or serve it just as it is.

Superfruits salad

The fruits in this delicious salad are bursting with flavour and will help to keep the body firing on all cylinders.

3 **POINTS** values per recipe • **93** Calories per serving • Takes 7 minutes • **Y** Vegan

½ mango (approx 150 g)
juice of ½ a lime
1 papaya, de-seeded, peeled and chopped roughly
1 kiwi, peeled and cut into half moon slices
50 g (1¾ oz) fresh blueberries

❶ In a blender (or in a jug with a hand held blender), purée the mango with the lime juice. Drizzle this over the other prepared fruits.

Strawberry and mango smoothie

Create this fabulous smoothie for breakfast or brunch and enjoy two of your Five-A-Day fruit and vegetable portions.

3½ **POINTS** values per recipe • 209 Calories per serving • Takes 5 minutes • **Y**

100 g (3½ oz) strawberries, stalks removed
½ mango, peeled and chopped, reserving
   one slice
4 tablespoons low fat natural yogurt
1 teaspoon vanilla essence
200 ml (7 fl oz) skimmed milk
a couple of ice cubes (optional)

❶ Reserve one strawberry and a slice of mango for decoration. Put the rest of the strawberries, mango, yogurt, vanilla essence and milk into a blender and process for 15–20 seconds, until smooth. If you prefer, use a hand held blender.
❷ Pour into a glass, adding a couple of ice cubes, if you like. Serve immediately.

TIP To make this smoothie more filling, slice in a small **banana** before blending, for an additional 1 **POINTS** value.

Italian ham, fig and ricotta

3½ **POINTS** values per recipe • 113 Calories per serving • Takes 2 minutes

2 fresh figs, halved
40 g (1½ oz) ricotta cheese
1 thin slice of **Parma ham**, sliced in half lengthways

❶ Arrange the ingredients together on a plate, think of Italian summers and enjoy.

Power porridge

Porridge is quick and easy to make and will set you up for the whole morning. With the addition of some fresh fruit and calcium-rich milk, porridge is also one of the best nutritional breakfasts you can have.

4 **POINTS** values per recipe • 295 Calories per serving • Takes 5 minutes • Ⓨ

40 g (1½ oz) porridge oats
100 ml (3½ fl oz) skimmed milk
1 small banana
50 g (1¾ oz) blueberries

❶ Place the porridge oats in a pan and add 250 ml (9 fl oz) of water. Bring to the boil and then simmer for 3–4 minutes, until thick and creamy.
❷ Serve in a bowl, top with the milk and fruit then eat while hot.

TIP You can vary the fruit: try it with a fresh, sliced **peach** and 50 g (1¾ oz) **raspberries**, for the same **POINTS** values.

Breakfast muffin

A simply delicious fast fix to get you going in the morning.

4 **POINTS** values per recipe • 267 Calories per serving • Takes 5 minutes

1 English muffin, split
low fat cooking spray
1 egg
1 tomato, sliced thickly
30 g (1¼ oz) wafer thin smoked ham

❶ Lightly toast the muffin and keep warm.
❷ Spray a non stick frying pan with the cooking spray and fry the egg for 2–3 minutes, or until done to your liking.
❸ Pile the tomato and ham on to one half of the muffin, add the egg and the muffin top. Serve immediately.

VARIATION For a vegetarian alternative, replace the ham with a grilled flat **mushroom**. This will reduce the **POINTS** value to 3½.

Full English breakfast

Yes, you can enjoy a full English – if you make a few adjustments to the cooking method.

4 **POINTS** values per recipe • 206 Calories per serving • Takes 20 minutes

1 x 40 g (1½ oz) thick low fat sausages
75 g (2¾ oz) mushrooms
50 ml (2 fl oz) vegetable stock
1 rasher lean back bacon
1 large tomato, halved
low fat cooking spray
1 egg
salt and freshly ground black pepper

❶ Preheat the grill to medium. Place the sausage on the grill pan and cook it for about 10 minutes, turning often.
❷ Meanwhile, put the mushrooms into a saucepan and add the stock. Simmer gently whilst cooking the rest of the meal.
❸ Arrange the bacon rasher and tomato halves on the grill pan with the sausage. Continue to cook until the bacon is crispy.
❹ Meanwhile, spray a non stick frying pan with the cooking spray. Heat for a few seconds, then crack in the egg. Cook over a medium heat for 2 minutes, then finish it off under the grill whilst you place the sausage, bacon, tomato and mushrooms on to a warm serving plate. Slide the egg on to the plate, season, then serve.

SERVING SUGGESTION Enjoy your breakfast with a medium slice of toast, if you like, for an additional 1 **POINTS** value.

Mushroom frittata

1½ **POINTS** values per recipe • **142** Calories per serving • Takes 25 minutes • Ⓨ

low fat cooking spray
1 **garlic clove**, chopped finely
250 g (9 oz) **mushrooms**, sliced
1 lemon wedge
1 egg
1 egg white
a few sprigs of fresh **parsley** or **thyme**, chopped
salt and freshly ground black pepper

❶ Heat a small, non stick frying pan and spray with the cooking spray, then stir fry the garlic for a minute until golden. With the heat on high, add the mushrooms and stir fry for a minute. Season, then squeeze the lemon wedge over them.

❷ Preheat the grill to high. Beat the egg and egg white together with the parsley or thyme in a small bowl until frothy. Then turn down the heat and add to the mushrooms. Cook for 1–2 minutes until the base of the frittata has set.

❸ Place the frying pan under the grill and brown the top. Cut into wedges to serve.

Breakfast omelette

2½ **POINTS** values per recipe • **200** Calories per serving • Takes 10 minutes • Ⓨ

low fat cooking spray
80 g (3 oz) button **mushrooms**, quartered
5 cherry **tomatoes**, halved
2 eggs
salt and freshly ground black pepper

❶ Lightly coat a non stick frying pan with the cooking spray and cook the mushrooms for 2 minutes, then add the tomatoes.
❷ Beat the eggs with 1 tablespoon of water and seasoning, then pour into the pan. Tip the pan from side to side to spread the egg around, then cook gently for 1½–2 minutes, or until set to your liking. Carefully fold over and serve on a warmed plate.

Croque monsieur

An adapted version of the usually very high fat French breakfast, this croque monsieur is a satisfying treat.

3½ **POINTS** values per recipe • **160** Calories per serving • Takes 10 minutes

1 medium slice wholemeal bread
25 g (1 oz) **low fat soft cheese with garlic and herbs**
40 g (1½ oz) **wafer thin ham**
15 g (½ oz) **half fat Cheddar cheese**

❶ Preheat the grill to medium and toast one side of the bread.
❷ Spread the untoasted side of the bread with the soft cheese and then cover with the ham and sprinkle with the Cheddar cheese.
❸ Grill until golden and bubbling and eat immediately.

Ⓨ **VARIATION** For a vegetarian alternative, replace the ham with a sliced **tomato** and 1 tablespoon of chutney. The **POINTS** values will remain the same.

Full English frittata

Fancy the whole works for breakfast without all the fat and calories? Try this satisfying frittata.

3½ **POINTS** values per recipe • **262** Calories per serving • Takes 10 minutes

2 turkey rashers
1 tomato, halved
3–4 mushrooms, depending on preference
low fat cooking spray
2 eggs
2 tablespoons skimmed milk
salt and freshly ground black pepper

❶ Preheat the grill to medium. Place the turkey rashers on a grill pan and grill for 1 minute on each side. At the same time, grill the tomato halves and mushrooms. Keep the grill switched on.
❷ Heat a medium, non stick frying pan and spray with the cooking spray. Add the turkey rashers, tomatoes and mushrooms.
❸ Beat the eggs with the milk and pour into the pan. Season. Cook over a medium heat to set the base of the frittata, then transfer to the grill for another few seconds to set the surface.
❹ Slide the frittata from the pan on to a warm plate and eat at once.

Parsnip cakes with poached egg

4 **POINTS** values per recipe • **292** Calories per serving • Takes 15 minutes • **Ⓥ**

low fat cooking spray
1 teaspoon vinegar (any type)
1 egg
freshly ground black pepper
a handful of fresh parsley, chopped, to garnish (optional)

FOR THE PARSNIP CAKES
150 g (5½ oz) parsnips, peeled and grated coarsely
½ onion, grated coarsely
1 garlic clove, crushed
a few sprigs of fresh thyme, woody stems removed, chopped finely
1 egg, beaten

❶ Place all the ingredients for the parsnip cakes in a bowl and mix together.
❷ Heat a large, non stick frying pan and spray with the cooking spray. Place four spoonfuls of the parsnip mixture well apart in the pan, and flatten into thin rounds with a fish slice or the back of a spoon.
❸ Fry on a low to medium heat for about 3–4 minutes until golden brown, then turn over and cook for another 4 minutes. Transfer the cakes to a plate and keep warm while you cook the rest of the mixture the same way.
❹ To poach the egg, bring a pan of water to the boil and add the vinegar. Break the egg into a mug and set aside. Using a spoon, swirl the water to create a whirlpool and gently slip in the egg. Reduce the water to a gentle simmer and cook for 3–4 minutes or until the egg is cooked to your liking, then fish out with a slotted spoon.
❺ Serve the egg on a pile of parsnip cakes with freshly ground black pepper and a scattering of parsley, if using.

Poached egg and smoked salmon brunch

What luxury. A special breakfast or brunch to enjoy on a lazy Sunday.

4 POINTS values per recipe • **232** Calories per serving • Takes 15 minutes

½ **teaspoon vinegar**
1 **egg**
1 **medium slice wholemeal bread**
50 g (1¾ oz) **smoked salmon**
1 **tablespoon caviar or salmon roe**
salt and freshly ground black pepper
a few sprigs of fresh dill, to garnish

❶ Bring a pan of water to the boil and add the vinegar. Break the egg into a mug and set aside. Using a spoon, swirl the water to create a whirlpool and gently slip in the egg. Reduce the water to a gentle simmer and cook for 3–4 minutes or until the egg is cooked to your liking. Meanwhile, toast the bread.
❷ Put the toast on to a serving plate and arrange the smoked salmon on top.
❸ Using a slotted spoon, remove the egg and place on top of the salmon, then spoon the caviar or salmon roe on top. Season, then serve, garnished with dill.

Red pepper and sweetcorn fritters

These little pancakes are great with a fresh tomato salsa made with a seasoned medley of chopped **tomato**, *finely diced red* **onion**, *fresh* **herbs** *and a drizzle of balsamic vinegar.*

5½ **POINTS** values per recipe • 370 Calories per serving • Takes 30 minutes • Ⓨ

2 tablespoons plain flour
1 egg, separated
2 tablespoons skimmed milk
a pinch of salt
½ red pepper, de–seeded and chopped finely
1 x 200 g can sweetcorn, drained
low fat cooking spray

❶ Put the flour, egg yolk and milk, with a pinch of salt, in a bowl and mix thoroughly.
❷ Stir in the pepper and sweetcorn. In a clean, grease-free bowl, whisk the egg white until stiff and fluffy and then gently fold it into the sweetcorn mixture with a large metal spoon.
❸ Heat a large, non stick frying pan and spray with the cooking spray, and then carefully add tablespoons of the batter to make small, drop scone–like pancakes.
❹ Cook two to three fritters at the same time, for 2–4 minutes, and then flip them over with a palette knife or fish slice and cook the other side for 2–4 minutes, until golden brown. Put them on a plate (the mixture makes four fritters) and keep warm while you cook the others. Serve immediately.

Fruity couscous

5½ **POINTS** values per recipe • 340 Calories per serving • Takes 10 minutes • Ⓨ Vegan

150 ml (5 fl oz) fresh orange juice
60 g (2 oz) dried couscous
1 eating apple, cored and grated
50 g (1¾ oz) fresh raspberries
½ tablespoon pumpkin seeds
½ tablespoon sunflower seeds

❶ Put the orange juice in a small lidded pan and bring to the boil. Add the couscous. Remove from the heat and cover.
❷ Leave for 5–7 minutes until swollen and most of the liquid has been absorbed.
❸ Stir in the grated apple and spoon into a bowl. Scatter over the raspberries and seeds and serve.

A change from traditional sandwiches, here you'll find a range of filling alternatives suitable for during the week and at weekends, that are certain to transform your lunchtimes.

Spanish style garlic prawns

A super speedy recipe that's ideal when you are hungry and want a hot filling meal in a hurry. Serve with 150 g (5½ oz) cooked **brown rice**, for an extra 3 **POINTS** values.

2 **POINTS** values per recipe • **211** Calories per serving • Takes 10 minutes

a pinch of saffron threads
50 ml (2 fl oz) dry or medium sherry
low fat cooking spray
1 yellow pepper, de-seeded and sliced
1 garlic clove, sliced
½ red chilli, de-seeded and sliced
1 x 230 g can chopped tomatoes
100 g (3½ oz) frozen raw peeled tiger
    prawns, thoroughly defrosted
freshly ground black pepper
1 tablespoon chopped fresh flat leaf parsley
    (optional)

❶ Crumble the saffron threads into the sherry and set aside until ready to use.
❷ Heat a non stick frying pan and spray with the cooking spray. Add the pepper and fry for 2 minutes. Add a splash of water if it starts to stick.
❸ Stir in the garlic and chilli and fry for 30 seconds or until the garlic is golden. Add the tomatoes, prawns and sherry mixture to the pan.
❹ Stir fry for 2–3 minutes or until the prawns are pink and firm. Season with freshly ground black pepper and scatter with the parsley before serving (if using).

TIP Sherry gives this dish an authentically Spanish flavour, but if you don't like using alcohol, use vegetable stock instead. This will also save 1 **POINTS** value.

Bhuna prawns

*The ideal topping for three **wholewheat crispbreads** for an added **POINTS** value of 2½, or spoon into a 225 g (8 oz) jacket **potato**, for an extra 2½ **POINTS** values.*

2½ **POINTS** values per recipe • 126 Calories per serving • Takes 6 minutes

2 tablespoons low fat natural yogurt
1 tablespoon low fat soft cheese
1 teaspoon Madras curry powder
60 g (2 oz) small cooked prawns
1 tomato, de-seeded and diced
50 g (1¾ oz) cucumber, diced finely
1 tablespoon chopped fresh coriander
1 spring onion, sliced finely
a squeeze of lemon juice
a few drops of Tabasco
salt and freshly ground black pepper

❶ Put the yogurt, soft cheese and curry powder in a bowl and mix until smooth.
❷ Fold in the prawns, tomato, cucumber, coriander and spring onion.
❸ Season to taste with lemon juice, Tabasco and seasoning.

Chilli tuna filling

*Spoon this zingy tuna filling on to a crisp-skinned 225 g (8 oz) jacket **potato** or into a toasted pitta bread with crunchy **salad leaves**, either one for an additional 2½ **POINTS** values.*

2½ **POINTS** values per recipe • 166 Calories per serving • Takes 5 minutes

1 x 80 g can tuna in brine, drained
1 tablespoon low fat natural yogurt
1 tablespoon low fat mayonnaise
1 tablespoon sweet chilli sauce
1 tablespoon chopped fresh coriander
½ tablespoon lime juice
salt and freshly ground black pepper

❶ Flake the tuna into a bowl, add the remaining ingredients and mix well. Season to taste.

Quick chilli bean filling

If you want to, double up the recipe and save one portion for another day.

3 POINTS values per recipe • **209** Calories per serving • Takes 10 minutes • Ⓨ ✳

low fat cooking spray
½ small yellow or green pepper, de-seeded and diced finely
1 garlic clove, crushed
a pinch of chilli powder
½ teaspoon ground cumin
1 x 230 g can chopped tomatoes
½ x 410 g can butter beans, drained and rinsed
2 tablespoons low fat plain fromage frais
1 tablespoon chopped fresh coriander

❶ Spray a non stick pan with the cooking spray and stir fry the pepper for 3 minutes until browned.
❷ Add the garlic, chilli powder and cumin and cook for 30 seconds before mixing in the tomatoes and butter beans. Simmer for 5 minutes.
❸ Serve immediately, topped with the fromage frais and coriander.

SERVING SUGGESTIONS Serve with a 225 g (8 oz) jacket **potato** for an additional 2½ **POINTS** values or with 150 g (5½ oz) cooked **brown rice** for an additional 3 **POINTS** values.

Tuna and bean croquettes

3½ **POINTS** values per recipe • 262 Calories per serving • Takes 15 minutes • ✳

100 g (3½ oz) leftover boiled potatoes
40 g (1½ oz) canned cannellini beans, drained
100 g (3½ oz) tuna in spring water, drained
2 gherkins, chopped finely
2 teaspoons lemon juice
1 spring onion, chopped finely
2 tablespoons chopped fresh parsley
1 tablespoon fresh breadcrumbs
low fat cooking spray
4 tablespoons passata
salt and freshly ground black pepper
zero **POINTS** value salad, to serve

❶ Use a fork to mash the potatoes, beans and tuna together. Add the gherkins, lemon juice, spring onion, 1 tablespoon of parsley and mash together again. Season to taste.

❷ Divide the mixture in to three and use your hands to roll into three sausage shapes on a flat surface. Scatter the breadcrumbs on to a plate and gently roll the croquettes in the crumbs to coat them. Reserve any leftover crumbs for later.

❸ Heat a non stick frying pan to a high heat and spray with the cooking spray. Heat the croquettes through for about 5 minutes. Respray the pan (or croquettes) occasionally as you roll them, until they are golden brown all over.

❹ Remove the croquettes and put on to a plate with the zero **POINTS** value salad.

❺ Reduce the heat and add the passata, remaining parsley and any leftover breadcrumbs to the pan. Heat through briefly, stirring well, and drizzle the croquettes with the tomato sauce.

Chick pea and tuna salad

A brilliant mixture of flavours, textures and colours, this filling salad looks just as good as it tastes.

3½ **POINTS** values per recipe • **300** Calories per serving • Takes 20 minutes

1 red pepper, de-seeded and quartered
125 g (4½ oz) green beans, trimmed and
 halved
juice of ½ a lemon
¼ teaspoon ground cumin
¼ teaspoon smoked paprika
½ x 410 g can chick peas, drained and rinsed
1 x 80 g can tuna in brine, drained
15 g (½ oz) wild rocket
salt and freshly ground black pepper

❶ Preheat the grill to its highest setting.
❷ Place the pepper on the grill rack and grill for 8–10 minutes until charred. Transfer to a bowl, cover and leave to cool slightly. When cool enough to handle, peel off and discard the skin, de-seed and roughly chop the flesh.
❸ Meanwhile, bring a pan of water to the boil and cook the green beans for 3–4 minutes until tender. Drain and rinse in cold water to stop the cooking process.
❹ Mix the lemon juice, cumin, paprika and seasoning together in a bowl. Add the green beans, chopped pepper, chick peas and tuna, and mix together well. Serve topped with the wild rocket.

Pasta and sweetcorn salad

This recipe is just as easy to prepare as sandwiches – and very satisfying. It's also ideal for picnics and can very easily be multiplied to make extra servings.

3½ **POINTS** values per recipe • **272** Calories per serving • Takes 15 minutes • **Y**

30 g (1¼ oz) dried pasta shells
50 g (1¾ oz) cherry tomatoes, halved
3 spring onions, chopped
5 cm (2 inches) cucumber, diced
2 tablespoons sweetcorn
1 celery stick, chopped finely
½ small orange or red pepper, de-seeded
 and diced
1 tablespoon low fat natural yogurt
1 tablespoon low fat mayonnaise
½ tablespoon parsley or chives, chopped,
 plus extra to garnish
3 olives in brine
salt and freshly ground black pepper

❶ Bring a pan of water to the boil. Add the pasta, bring back to the boil and cook according to the packet instructions. Drain, reserving ½ a tablespoon of cooking liquid.
❷ Prepare all the salad vegetables and put them in a large salad bowl or lidded plastic box.
❸ Mix the pasta in with the salad vegetables and set aside.
❹ Add the yogurt and mayonnaise to the reserved pasta water with some seasoning and mix together thoroughly – a mini whisk makes this very quick. Add the herbs, reserving some for the garnish.
❺ Stir the sauce straight into the pasta salad and top with the remaining herbs and olives.

Oriental chicken salad

A quick and easy salad with lovely unusual flavours.

4 POINTS values per recipe • **230** Calories per serving • Takes 15 minutes

50 g (1¾ oz) dried glass noodles, soaked and
   drained
low fat cooking spray
1 cm (½ inch) fresh root ginger, peeled and
   grated
100 g (3½ oz) skinless boneless chicken
   breast, sliced into thin strips
1 tablespoon light soy sauce
2 spring onions, sliced finely
½ green pepper, de-seeded and chopped
   finely
½ red pepper, de-seeded and chopped finely
juice of a lime
1 small green chilli, de-seeded and chopped
   finely (optional)
a small bunch of fresh coriander or basil,
   chopped

❶ Cook the noodles in boiling water for
3–4 minutes, and then drain and rinse them
under cold water to prevent them from
cooking further.
❷ Put the noodles in a large bowl and snip
them with scissors to make smaller lengths.
❸ Spray a non stick frying pan with the cooking
spray and fry the ginger for a few seconds. Add
the chicken and stir fry for 5 minutes, until it is
cooked through and golden.
❹ Add the soy sauce and stir fry a further
30 seconds then pour everything in the
pan over the noodles in the bowl. Add all the
other ingredients and toss together. Serve in
warm bowls.

Chinese chicken noodle soup

This Chinese style favourite makes for a quick and very filling lunch or light supper.

4 *POINTS* values per recipe • **268** Calories per serving • Takes 6 minutes

40 g (1½ oz) fine egg noodles, broken roughly
60 g (2 oz) baby corn, sliced thinly
½ chicken stock cube, made up to 300 ml
   (10 fl oz) with boiling water
1 teaspoon soy sauce
75 g (2¾ oz) cooked skinless boneless
   chicken breast, sliced
2 spring onions, sliced

❶ Add the noodles and baby corn to a pan of boiling water and cook for 3 minutes. Drain and rinse in cold water.

❷ Pour the stock into a saucepan, add the soy sauce and bring to a simmer. Mix in the chicken, spring onions, cooked noodles and baby corn and heat through for 1–2 minutes until piping hot. Pour into a bowl and serve.

❸ VARIATION For a vegetarian version, replace the cooked chicken with the same weight of sliced button **mushrooms** and use vegetable stock in place of the chicken stock. This will be a ***POINTS*** value of 2.

Thai beef salad

Traditionally a Thai starter, this main meal sized salad is a wonderful combination of sweet and sharp flavours.

4 *POINTS* values per recipe • **284** Calories per serving • Takes 15 minutes

125 g (4½ oz) piece of beef medallion or lean fillet steak at room temperature
low fat cooking spray
1 tablespoon Thai fish sauce or soy sauce
juice of ½ a lime
1 teaspoon grated fresh root ginger
4 cm (1½ inch) piece of cucumber, cut into matchsticks
50 g (1¾ oz) fresh beansprouts, rinsed
60 g (2 oz) seedless red grapes, halved
½ red chilli, de-seeded and sliced
1 tablespoon fresh mint leaves
30 g (1¼ oz) herb salad

❶ Preheat a griddle pan or non stick frying pan on a high setting. Lightly spray the steak with the cooking spray and add to the pan. Cook for 2 minutes on each side for rare or 3 minutes on each side for medium rare. Remove the cooked steak to a plate and rest for 5 minutes before slicing thinly.
❷ Meanwhile, mix the fish or soy sauce with the lime juice in a salad bowl. Squeeze the grated ginger over the bowl to extract the juice and then discard the pulp. Toss the cucumber and beansprouts into the dressing. Add the grapes, chilli, mint leaves and herb salad and mix thoroughly. Transfer to a plate.
❸ Arrange the steak on top of the salad, pouring any juices from the plate over the top. Serve immediately.

TIP For the best results, the steak should be cooked rare to medium rare in this recipe in order to keep the meat succulent and juicy.

Lamb chop with a fruity glaze

*A mustard and redcurrant glaze makes this lamb chop taste truly wonderful. For a more substantial meal, serve with 100 g (3½ oz) mashed **potato** made up with 1 tablespoon **skimmed milk**, and some lightly boiled **Savoy cabbage**, for an extra 1 **POINTS** value.*

4 *POINTS* values per recipe • **273** Calories per serving • Takes 25 minutes

150 g (5½ oz) lamb chop, trimmed of all fat
¼ teaspoon dried thyme
1 level teaspoon coarse grain mustard
1 teaspoon redcurrant jelly
½ teaspoon lemon juice
salt and freshly ground black pepper

❶ Preheat the grill until piping hot. Sprinkle the chop with the thyme and season with freshly ground black pepper.
❷ Put the chop on the grill rack and turn the heat down to medium. Grill for about 5–7 minutes on each side depending on whether you like lamb medium or well done.
❸ Meanwhile, mix the mustard, redcurrant jelly and lemon juice together. About 4 minutes from the end of cooking on the second side, spoon the glaze on to the chop.
❹ Return to the grill to finish cooking. Season and serve.

Spicy vegetable stir fry (4 POINTS VALUE)

4 POINTS values per recipe • **374** Calories per serving •
Takes 20 minutes • **Y** Vegan

100 g (3½ oz) new potatoes, scrubbed and
  diced
25 g (1 oz) cashew nuts
low fat cooking spray
1 onion, sliced
1½ teaspoons mustard seeds
½ green chilli, sliced
75 g (2¾ oz) white cabbage, shredded
½ green pepper, de-seeded and sliced
1 courgette, sliced on the diagonal
2 garlic cloves, chopped
4 curry leaves (optional)
5 cherry tomatoes, halved
a squeeze of lemon juice
salt and freshly ground black pepper

❶ Bring a pan of water to the boil and cook the potatoes until tender. Drain and set aside.
❷ Meanwhile, toast the cashews in a dry wok or large frying pan until slightly golden. Set them aside too.
❸ Spray the wok or frying pan with the cooking spray and stir fry the onion for 3 minutes.
Add the mustard seeds, followed by the chilli, cabbage, green pepper, courgette, garlic and curry leaves (if using). Stir fry for 3 minutes.
❹ Add 6 tablespoons of water, the cooked potatoes and tomatoes, season and cook for another minute. Squeeze in the lemon juice and scatter with the cashew nuts before serving.

Sun dried tomato pasta salad

4 **POINTS** values per recipe • 270 Calories per serving • Takes 20 minutes • Ⓨ

40 g (1½ oz) small pasta shapes
25 g (1 oz) mange tout, sliced diagonally
2 sun-dried tomatoes in oil, rinsed gently and sliced thinly
2 teaspoons oil from the jar of sun-dried tomatoes
25 g (1 oz) rocket leaves or watercress
salt and freshly ground black pepper

❶ Bring a large pan of water to the boil, add the pasta and cook according to the packet instructions. Add the mange tout to the pan for the last 2–3 minutes and cook until just tender. Drain and rinse the pasta and mange tout in cold water.

❷ Mix together the pasta, mange tout, sun-dried tomatoes and oil. Season and top with the rocket leaves or watercress before serving.

Avocado wrap

4½ **POINTS** values per recipe • **251** Calories per serving • Takes 5–10 minutes + optional chilling • Ⓥ

4 Little Gem lettuce leaves, shredded
¼ avocado, cut into small chunks
1 tablespoon Weight Watchers Reduced Fat Mayonnaise
1 tablespoon low fat natural yogurt
1 soft tortilla wrap
½ tablespoon cress
a zero **POINTS** value salad, to serve

❶ Put the shredded lettuce and avocado into a small bowl. In a ramekin, mix the mayonnaise with the yogurt. Pour the mayonnaise mixture over the lettuce and avocado and carefully combine.
❷ Lay some clingfilm on a flat surface and place the tortilla wrap on it. Spoon the lettuce mixture in a strip along the centre of the wrap. Sprinkle it with the cress and then fold the two sides over the filling to form a tube. Hold it firmly together until you can wrap the clingfilm round the tortilla and seal well. If you have time, chill in the fridge for at least an hour.
❸ Remove the clingfilm and make a diagonal cut across the centre of the wrap. Serve the two halves with the zero **POINTS** value salad.

Fattoush

4½ **POINTS** values per recipe • **321** Calories per serving • Takes 10 minutes • Ⓥ

1 mini pitta bread, split in half
9 cm (3½ inches) cucumber, quartered lengthways, de-seeded and chopped
2 spring onions, sliced
3 vine ripened tomatoes, quartered
6 pitted black olives in brine, halved
2 tablespoons pomegranate seeds (about a quarter of a pomegranate)
50 g (1¾ oz) light Feta, cubed

FOR THE DRESSING
1 teaspoon extra virgin olive oil
1 tablespoon lemon juice
a pinch of ground cumin
salt and freshly ground black pepper

❶ Preheat the grill to medium then toast each half of the pitta bread until golden and crisp. When cool, break the pitta into pieces of varying size.
❷ Meanwhile, to make the dressing, mix together all the ingredients in a bowl then season.
❸ Put the cucumber, spring onions, tomatoes, olives and pitta bread in a shallow dish. Pour the dressing over and toss to coat the vegetables. Sprinkle over the pomegranate seeds and Feta before serving.

Cajun steak muffin

A great treat for a speedy lunch, especially at the weekend.

4½ **POINTS** values per recipe • 247 Calories per serving • Takes 6 minutes

¼–½ teaspoon Cajun spice mix
60 g (2 oz) sandwich steak or minute steak, trimmed
low fat cooking spray
1 white or wholemeal English muffin, split
1 tablespoon 0% fat Greek yogurt
1 tomato, sliced
1 leaf from a round lettuce or shredded Iceberg lettuce

❶ Sprinkle the Cajun spice mix (use ¼ or ½ teaspoon, depending on desired degree of spiciness) over both sides of the steak.
❷ Preheat a non stick frying pan and lightly coat with the cooking spray. Fry the steak for 1–1½ minutes on each side, to your liking.
❸ Meanwhile, lightly toast the muffin then spread the yogurt on to the cut sides. Top with the sliced tomato, lettuce and steak and eat immediately.

Ⓥ **VARIATION** For a vegetarian version, replace the steak with a large flat **mushroom**, sliced and fried as above. This will be a **POINTS** value of 2½.

Smoked salmon pitta pizza

This makes a quick and satisfying lunch.

5 **POINTS** values per recipe • 235 Calories per serving • Takes 5 minutes to prepare, 15 minutes to cook

1 pitta bread
2 teaspoons low fat soft cheese with garlic and herbs
50 g (1¾ oz) sliced smoked salmon
¼ red onion, sliced finely
1 teaspoon baby capers in brine, drained and rinsed
a handful of rocket leaves
freshly ground black pepper
1 lemon wedge, to serve

❶ Preheat the oven to Gas Mark 4/180°C/ fan oven 160°C. Spread the pitta with the soft cheese, top with salmon slices and scatter with the onion and capers.
❷ Bake for 10–15 minutes, until the edges of the pitta bread are crispy. Garnish with the rocket leaves and freshly ground black pepper. Serve with the lemon wedge to squeeze over.

TIP Salad leaves are a great way to add interest and bulk to your meals, without adding any **POINTS** values. Try to vary the salad leaves you buy, until you find one you like. Rocket, as used in this recipe, has a nutty, peppery flavour that works well with cheese or fish.

Creamy carbonara tagliatelle

5 *POINTS* values per recipe • **284** Calories per serving • Takes 15 minutes

40 g (1½ oz) tagliatelle
1 rasher lean back bacon, chopped finely
2 tablespoons skimmed milk
1 egg, beaten
1 tablespoon chopped fresh parsley
freshly ground black pepper

❶ Bring a large pan of water to the boil and cook the pasta according to the packet instructions. Drain.
❷ Meanwhile, heat a small pan, add the bacon and stir fry for 3–4 minutes until crispy. Beat the milk into the egg and add to the bacon. Cook, stirring for about 30 seconds and remove from the heat.
❸ Toss in the pasta, stirring to coat. Return to the heat and cook for 1–2 minutes until the sauce has thickened slightly but still remains creamy. Serve in a warmed bowl, garnished with the parsley and plenty of freshly ground black pepper.

Club sandwich

5 *POINTS* values per recipe • **354** Calories per serving • Takes 10 minutes

1 tablespoon Weight Watchers Reduced Fat Mayonnaise
1 egg, hard boiled and mashed
3 slices low calorie bread, toasted lightly
1 crunchy lettuce leaf, such as Iceberg, shredded
2 bacon medallions or turkey rashers, grilled
1 tomato, sliced
salt and freshly ground black pepper
a zero *POINTS* value salad, to serve

❶ Mix half a tablespoon of the mayonnaise with the mashed egg and a little seasoning. Spread the remaining mayonnaise on to one side of two of the pieces of toast.
❷ Top the plain slice of toast with the egg mix and some lettuce. Cover with a second piece of toast (mayonnaise side facing up) and top that with bacon and the slices of tomato. Finish with the final piece of toast.
❸ Gently press down on the sandwich and secure with four cocktail sticks. Cut diagonally between the cocktail sticks to form four tall, triangular sandwiches. Serve with the zero *POINTS* value salad.

Leek and ham with hollandaise sauce

6 POINTS values per recipe • **362** Calories per serving • Takes 20 minutes

150 g (5½ oz) new potatoes
2 leeks, trimmed well
1 egg yolk
2 tablespoons low fat plain fromage frais
1 tablespoon white wine vinegar
2 x 30 g (1¼ oz) slices of ham
salt and freshly ground black pepper

❶ Bring a large pan of water to the boil. Add the potatoes and leeks and simmer for 15 minutes.
❷ Meanwhile, for the sauce, put the egg yolk in a small non stick pan with 1 tablespoon of the fromage frais, the white wine vinegar and some seasoning. Heat very gently (or the egg will scramble), stirring all the time until the sauce thickens. Remove from the heat and stir in the remaining fromage frais.
❸ When the leeks are cooked, remove them to a plate with a slotted spoon (leave the potatoes for a few minutes more unless they are already tender). Carefully wrap a slice of ham around each leek.
❹ Pour the sauce over the leeks and ham and serve with the potatoes.

VARIATION You can substitute **chicory** for the leeks, but allow 20 minutes cooking time. The hollandaise sauce also goes really well with hot or cold **salmon**.

Curried chicken pasta salad lunchbox

Substantial salads are ideal for lunch, whether you eat at home or at work. This mildly spiced pasta salad will keep you satisfied all afternoon.

6½ POINTS values per recipe • **449** Calories per serving • Takes 20 minutes

60 g (2 oz) dried pasta twists
low fat cooking spray
100 g (3½ oz) skinless boneless chicken breast
½ teaspoon curry powder
a pinch of ground turmeric
1 teaspoon lemon juice
30 g (1¼ oz) low fat soft cheese
125 g (4½ oz) low fat natural yogurt
1 teaspoon artificial sweetener
½ red, yellow or orange pepper, de-seeded and diced
2 spring onions, chopped roughly
2 tablespoons chopped fresh coriander

❶ Bring a pan of water to the boil and cook the pasta for 10–12 minutes or according to the packet instructions. Drain and rinse in cold water.
❷ Meanwhile, spray a non stick frying pan with the cooking spray and cook the chicken for 5 minutes on each side or until cooked through. Remove from the pan and slice when cooled.
❸ Mix the curry powder, turmeric and lemon juice together to make a paste. Blend in the soft cheese until smooth. Add the yogurt and sweetener and mix together well.
❹ Stir in the remaining ingredients, including the pasta and chicken, until everything is well coated in the dressing. Transfer to a lunchbox, seal and chill until ready to serve.

Ⓥ **VARIATION** For a vegetarian version, use 100 g (3½ oz) **Quorn fillets** in place of the chicken. The **POINTS** values will be 6.

Perfect for a night in after a busy day. A choice of easy to prepare, satisfying recipes that are certain to inspire. Make the most of the time you have for yourself.

Sizzling steak stir fry

*Sometimes only steak will do. This recipe will satisfy this need and your appetite. Serve with 150 g (5½ oz) cooked **brown basmati rice**, for an extra 3 **POINTS** values.*

2½ **POINTS** values per recipe • **285** Calories per serving • Takes 25 minutes • ✳

low fat cooking spray
2.5 cm (1 inch) fresh root ginger, grated finely
100 g (3½ oz) lean fillet or sirloin beef steak,
   all fat removed, cut into thin strips
2 tablespoons soy sauce
1 tablespoon tomato purée mixed with
   100 ml (3½ fl oz) water
4 spring onions
150 g (5½ oz) mushrooms, sliced
100 g (3½ oz) beansprouts
½ red pepper, de-seeded and sliced finely
a small bunch of coriander, chopped

❶ Heat a large, non stick pan or wok and spray with the cooking spray. Stir fry the ginger for 10 seconds and then add the steak and stir fry for 2 minutes, until it begins to brown.
❷ Add all the other ingredients and stir fry for 5 minutes, then serve.

TIP Opt for lean cuts of meat and always cut the fat off meats before eating – you'll be surprised how quickly you go off the taste of fat.

Baked haddock clementine

2½ **POINTS** values per recipe • 194 Calories per serving • Takes 10 minutes to prepare, 12 minutes to cook

1 x 150 g (5½ oz) haddock fillet, skinless
1 clementine, cut in half and one half peeled and cut into round slices, reserving the other half for squeezing over
2 spring onions, sliced finely
1 cm (½ inch) fresh root ginger, peeled and chopped finely
1 teaspoon soy sauce
1 teaspoon sesame oil
few sprigs of fresh coriander, to garnish (optional)

❶ Preheat the oven to Gas Mark 6/200°C/fan oven 180°C.
❷ Tear off a piece of non stick baking parchment about 30 cm (12 inches) and fold in half to make a square. Place the haddock in the middle.
❸ Arrange the clementine slices over the fish, then sprinkle over the spring onions and ginger. Squeeze the other half of the clementine over the fish, then drizzle over the soy sauce and sesame oil.
❹ Fold up the baking parchment, folding over at the top to seal, then tuck the ends under the fish.
❺ Place the parcel on a baking tray and bake for 12 minutes until the parcel is puffed up and golden. Open at the table to get the full benefit of the delicious smells. Garnish with coriander, if using.

SERVING SUGGESTION Serve with steamed vegetables, such as **carrot** matchsticks and shredded **cabbage**, for no extra **POINTS** values.

VARIATION This can be made with 150 g (5½ oz) **salmon** fillet instead, for 6 **POINTS** values.

Baked chilli egg

*An easy supper dish that can be rustled up with the minimum of effort yet looks and feels like a proper meal. Serve with a big green salad of interesting fresh leaves like **rocket**, **watercress**, **mizuna** or **lamb's lettuce**, for no extra **POINTS** values.*

2½ **POINTS** values per recipe • **250** Calories per serving • Takes 20 minutes to prepare, 20 minutes to cook

low fat cooking spray
1 shallot or small onion, chopped finely
1 garlic clove, crushed
1 x 200 g can chopped tomatoes
1 small chilli, de–seeded and chopped finely
1 teaspoon Worcestershire sauce
1 teaspoon soy sauce or tamari sauce
½ red pepper, de–seeded and diced finely
1 egg
4–5 asparagus spears, woody ends broken off, spears chopped but tops left whole
50 g (1¾ oz) lean ham, sliced into small strips
salt and freshly ground black pepper

❶ Heat a small saucepan and spray with the cooking spray. Stir fry the shallot or onion and garlic for a few minutes, until softened, adding a little water if they start to stick.
❷ Add the tomatoes, chilli, Worcestershire sauce, soy or tamari sauce, seasoning and pepper, stir together and bring to the boil. Simmer for 5 minutes, until reduced a little and thickened.
❸ Preheat the oven to Gas Mark 7/220°C/ fan oven 200°C. Tip the mixture into a small shallow ovenproof dish. Make a well in the centre of the sauce and break the egg into it.
❹ Scatter the asparagus and ham around on top of the sauce, season with freshly ground black pepper and bake for 15–20 minutes, until the egg is set.

Herb crusted baked chicken breast

*Another supremely quick and easy dinner idea. Serve with a 225 g (8 oz) baked **potato** and steamed **spring greens**, **cabbage** or **broccoli** with a drizzle of soy sauce, for an extra 2½ **POINTS** values.*

2½ **POINTS** values per recipe • **165** Calories per serving • Takes 10 minutes to prepare, 20 minutes to cook

1 x 150 g (5½ oz) skinless boneless chicken breast
a few sprigs of fresh parsley, basil or mint
a few sprigs of fresh thyme or rosemary
low fat cooking spray
250 ml (9 fl oz) vegetable or chicken stock
salt and freshly ground black pepper

❶ Preheat the oven to Gas Mark 6/200°C/fan oven 180°C. Make shallow cuts into the chicken with the tip of a sharp knife and place on a non stick baking tray.
❷ Mix the herbs and seasoning together in a small bowl and then spread this over the chicken and spray with the cooking spray. Pour the stock into the tray around the chicken.
❸ Bake for 20 minutes, until just cooked through and golden then serve with any juices left in the baking tray poured over.

Malaysian chicken

*Tantalise the taste buds with this deliciously different twist on chicken. Serve with 150 g (5½ oz) of cooked rice, for an extra 3 **POINTS** values, and a heap of steamed **broccoli**.*

2½ POINTS values per recipe • **211** Calories per serving • Takes 10 minutes to prepare, 12 minutes to cook

1 small onion, sliced
½ red chilli, de-seeded and chopped finely
low fat cooking spray
1 x 150 g (5½ oz) skinless boneless chicken
    breast, diced
1 teaspoon light brown soft sugar
2 teaspoons soy sauce
4 tablespoons chicken stock or water
1 teaspoon rice vinegar or lime juice

❶ Spray a lidded, non stick saucepan with the cooking spray and fry the onions and chilli for 2 minutes.
❷ Add the chicken and stir fry for 1 minute over a high heat, then sprinkle in the sugar and cook for 1 minute more until caramelised.
❸ In a jug, mix the soy sauce, stock and rice vinegar or lime juice together. Pour over the chicken, cover the pan and simmer gently for 10 minutes.
❹ Remove the lid, increase the heat, and bubble for 2 minutes until slightly reduced, tossing the chicken in the sauce to glaze.

Spiced korma plaice

*Ideal served with a **tomato**, **cucumber** and **onion** salad, for no additional **POINTS** values.*

2½ POINTS values per recipe • **158** Calories per serving • Takes 15 minutes

1 plaice fillet (approximately 175 g/6 oz)
1 tablespoon low fat natural yogurt
½ red chilli, de-seeded and sliced
1 tablespoon lime juice
½ teaspoon korma curry powder
a pinch of cumin seeds
low fat cooking spray
salt and freshly ground black pepper
1 tablespoon chopped fresh coriander, to
    garnish

❶ Preheat the grill to medium hot and line the grill pan with foil. Wash and pat dry the plaice fillet.
❷ Mix together the yogurt, half the chilli, lime juice, curry powder and cumin seeds in a small bowl. Season.
❸ Spray the foil with the cooking spray. Put the plaice fillet skin side up on the foil and grill for 4 minutes. Turn the fish over and spoon on the spicy yogurt mixture until the fillet is covered. Return to the grill for 4 minutes or until cooked.
❹ Serve sprinkled with the coriander and the remaining chilli.

Japanese shiitake noodles

This Japanese style noodle stir fry can be on the table in 15 minutes or less when you're in need of a speedy but wholesome home cooked meal.

3 **POINTS** values per recipe • **203** Calories per serving • Takes 15 minutes • Ⓨ

low fat cooking spray
150 g (5½ oz) shiitake mushrooms, halved through the stalk
1 small garlic clove, sliced finely
1 teaspoon shredded fresh root ginger
6 spring onions, trimmed and cut into thirds
2 tablespoons soy sauce, preferably Japanese
100 g (3½ oz) pak choi, separated into leaves
60 g (2 oz) soba noodles or medium egg noodles

❶ Spray a medium, lidded, non stick saucepan with the cooking spray then add the mushrooms, garlic, ginger and spring onions and stir fry for 3 minutes until browned.
❷ Add the soy sauce and 100 ml (3½ fl oz) water to the pan, bring to the boil and cook, stirring, for 5 minutes, uncovered, until around 3 tablespoons of syrupy liquid remain. Add the pak choi to the pan, cover and cook for 2 minutes or until the leaves begin to wilt.
❸ Meanwhile, bring a pan of water to the boil and cook the noodles according to the packet instructions. Drain the noodles and then toss together with the vegetables. Serve immediately.

VARIATION If shiitake mushrooms and pak choi aren't available, substitute chestnut **mushrooms** and roughly chopped **Chinese leaf** for a perfectly good alternative. The **POINTS** values will stay the same.

Penne forestière

Dried porcini mushrooms intensify the flavour of this pasta sauce, giving it a wonderful richness. Use open cup mushrooms rather than button mushrooms if you can.

3 POINTS values per recipe • **276** Calories per serving • Takes 8 minutes to prepare, 12 minutes to cook • Ⓥ • ✳

5 g (¼ oz) porcini mushrooms, snipped
½ onion, sliced
low fat cooking spray
1 garlic clove, crushed
150 g (5½ oz) fresh mushrooms, chopped roughly
½ x 400 g can chopped tomatoes
60 g (2 oz) penne
salt and freshly ground black pepper

❶ Place the porcini mushrooms in a small bowl, cover with 4 tablespoons boiling water and leave to soak and soften.
❷ In a non stick saucepan, fry the onion in the cooking spray for 4 minutes, adding a splash of water if needed to prevent the onions from sticking.
❸ Stir in the garlic, fresh mushrooms and 2 tablespoons of the porcini soaking liquid, and cook for 3 minutes, then add the tomatoes, porcini and the rest of the soaking liquid. Season and simmer for 12 minutes.
❹ Meanwhile, bring a pan of water to the boil and cook the penne for 10–12 minutes or according to the packet instructions until tender. Drain and mix with the sauce, then serve straight away.

Quick beef stroganoff

*This satisfying, savoury supper dish can be served on a bed of **tagliatelle** (60 g/2 oz dried weight) cooked according to the packet instructions, for an additional 3 **POINTS** values.*

3 POINTS values per recipe • **172** Calories per serving • Takes 10 minutes

low fat cooking spray
110 g (4 oz) lean stir fry beef or lean steak, cut into thin strips
75 g (2¾ oz) chestnut mushrooms, sliced
4 spring onions, sliced
a pinch of paprika
75 ml (3 fl oz) beef stock, made using ¼ stock cube
2 tablespoons very low fat plain fromage frais
salt and freshly ground black pepper

❶ Heat a non stick frying pan and lightly coat with the cooking spray. Add the beef, followed by the mushrooms and spring onions. Stir fry for 3 minutes. Sprinkle in the paprika then pour in the beef stock.
❷ Bubble rapidly for 30–60 seconds until the liquid is reduced and syrupy.
❸ Remove the pan from the heat and leave for about 1 minute, then stir in the fromage frais and seasoning to taste.

Ⓥ **VARIATION** For a vegetarian version, replace the beef with 250 g (9 oz) mixed **mushrooms**, and use vegetable stock instead of beef stock, for a **POINTS** value of ½.

47

Quorn Caesar pasta salad

3½ POINTS values per recipe • **257** Calories per serving • Takes 20 minutes • Ⓥ

40 g (1½ oz) fusilli, bucati, tubetti or macaroni
low fat cooking spray
75 g (2¾ oz) chicken flavoured Quorn pieces
2 tablespoons virtually fat free fromage frais
1 teaspoon wholegrain mustard
4 Cos lettuce leaves, shredded
4 cherry tomatoes, halved
salt and freshly ground black pepper

❶ Bring a large pan of water to the boil, add the pasta and cook according to the packet instructions. Drain and rinse in cold water.
❷ Heat a non stick frying pan, spray with the cooking spray and pan fry the Quorn pieces for 3–5 minutes until brown. Set aside.
❸ To make the dressing, mix together the fromage frais and mustard, season and set aside.
❹ Toss together the pasta, Quorn pieces, lettuce and tomatoes. Serve with the dressing drizzled over the top.

Lamb rogan josh

*A very spicy dish. Delicious served with 150 g (5½ oz) cooked **brown rice**, for an extra 3 **POINTS** values.*

4 POINTS values per recipe • **322** Calories per serving • Takes 20 minutes to prepare, 50 minutes to cook • ✳

1 cm (½ inch) fresh root ginger, peeled and chopped
2 garlic cloves, chopped finely
low fat cooking spray
4 cardamom pods, cracked
1 bay leaf
2 cm (¾ inch) cinnamon stick
175 g (6 oz) cubed shoulder of lamb
1 small onion, chopped finely
½ teaspoon ground cumin
½ teaspoon ground coriander
¼ teaspoon cayenne pepper
½ teaspoon paprika
1 teaspoon tomato purée
½ teaspoon salt

❶ Place the ginger and garlic in a small blender and blend to a paste with 2 teaspoons of water.
❷ Heat a lidded, non stick pan and spray with the cooking spray. Add the cardamom pods, bay leaf and cinnamon. Add the lamb pieces and brown all over. Remove the lamb with a slotted spoon and set aside.
❸ Add the onion to the pan and cook for 3–4 minutes until it begins to brown at the edges.
❹ Add the garlic and ginger paste from the blender to the onions. Stir for 30 seconds before adding the remaining spices and tomato purée.
❺ Return the lamb to the pan, add the salt and 100 ml (3½ fl oz) water. Stir well and bring to the boil.
❻ Cover and simmer gently for 40–50 minutes or until the meat is tender.

One pan turkey Bolognese

A healthy twist on the usual spaghetti Bolognese – and all cooked in just one pot.

4½ POINTS values per recipe • **395** Calories per serving • Takes 10 minutes to prepare, 15 minutes to cook

low fat cooking spray
1 small onion, chopped finely
1 garlic clove, crushed
100 g (3½ oz) turkey mince
100 ml (3½ fl oz) chicken stock
1 teaspoon tomato purée
1 teaspoon soy sauce
1 x 200 g can chopped tomatoes
50 g (1¾ oz) dried spaghetti, broken into short lengths
100 g (3½ oz) mixed zero **POINTS** value vegetables, chopped finely
salt and freshly ground black pepper

❶ Heat a lidded, non stick saucepan and spray with the cooking spray, then stir fry the onion and garlic for a few minutes until softened, adding a few tablespoons of the stock if necessary to prevent them from sticking.
❷ Add the turkey mince, season and stir fry for a further 3 minutes until it is browned and crumbly. Add all the other ingredients except for the vegetables and bring to the boil. Reduce the heat and simmer, covered, for 10 minutes.
❸ Add the vegetables and stir in, then simmer uncovered for 5 minutes more until the vegetables and pasta are cooked and serve.

Balti pork with chick peas

4½ **POINTS** values per recipe • 336 Calories per serving • Takes 25 minutes • ✳

low fat cooking spray
150 g (5½ oz) lean pork loin steak, sliced
   thinly across the grain
1 small onion, sliced thinly
½ red chilli, de-seeded and chopped
1 garlic clove, chopped
½ green pepper, de-seeded and sliced
1 tablespoon garam masala
1 tablespoon tomato purée
75 g (2¾ oz) canned no-sugar chick peas,
   drained and rinsed
1 teaspoon lemon juice
salt and freshly ground black pepper

❶ Heat a wok or non stick frying pan and spray with the cooking spray, add the pork and stir fry over a medium high heat for 2 minutes until browned all over. Remove to a separate plate using a slotted spoon.

❷ Re-spray the wok or pan with the cooking spray, add the onion and stir fry for 6 minutes until softened. Then add the chilli, garlic and pepper and stir fry for another minute.

❸ Return the pork to the wok or pan and stir in the garam masala, tomato purée, chick peas and 6 tablespoons of water. Cook over a medium low heat, stirring frequently, for 5 minutes. Stir in the lemon juice and a little extra water, if necessary, then season and serve.

Mushroom stroganoff

5 POINTS values per recipe • 237 Calories per serving •
Takes 20 minutes • Ⓨ

low fat cooking spray
1 onion, chopped finely
2 garlic cloves, chopped finely
225 g (8 oz) button mushrooms
100 ml (3½ fl oz) dry white wine
4 tablespoons vegetable stock
2½ tablespoons reduced fat crème fraîche
salt and freshly ground black pepper
1 tablespoon chopped fresh parsley,
   to garnish

❶ Spray a lidded, heavy based saucepan with the cooking spray and cook the onion for 7 minutes, adding a little water if necessary if it starts to stick. Add the garlic and mushrooms and fry for another 2 minutes.
❷ Pour in the wine and bring to the boil. Cook until the wine has almost evaporated and the smell of alcohol disappears. Add the stock and simmer, half covered, for 5 minutes.
❸ Remove the pan from the heat, season well and stir in the crème fraîche. Serve sprinkled with parsley.

SERVING SUGGESTION Serve with **green beans**, for no extra **POINTS** values.

Quick pesto pasta

The ultimate in quick, satisfying dinners, this is a bright and beautiful plate of crisp summer vegetables with pesto and pasta.

5 **POINTS** values per recipe • 412 Calories per serving • Takes 25 minutes • **Y** (if using vegetarian pesto sauce)

60 g (2 oz) dried pasta shapes
low fat cooking spray
100 g (3½ oz) snow peas
50 g (1¾ oz) frozen petits pois
100 g (3½ oz) broccoli
100 g (3½ oz) cherry tomatoes, halved
1 tablespoon pesto sauce
salt and freshly ground black pepper

❶ Bring a pan of water to the boil and cook the pasta according to the packet instructions. Drain, reserving 3 tablespoons of the cooking liquid.
❷ Heat a wok or large frying pan, spray with the cooking spray and then steam fry (see Tip) the pasta and vegetables with 3 tablespoons of water for 2–3 minutes.
❸ Add the pesto sauce and seasoning, heat through and then serve.

TIP To steam fry, turn the heat up to high and allow the pan to get hot. Spray with low fat cooking spray and then add a little water or stock. The water will turn to steam almost immediately and this will cook the food.

Veggie sausage and lentil conchiglie

5 **POINTS** values per recipe • 246 Calories per serving • Takes 15 minutes to prepare, 15 minutes to cook • **Y**

15 g (½ oz) Puy lentils
300 ml (10 fl oz) hot vegetable stock
1 garlic clove, sliced
1 sprig of fresh thyme
50 g (1¾ oz) green beans, trimmed and halved
40 g (1½ oz) conchiglie
2 vegetarian sausages, grilled and chopped

❶ In a lidded, non stick pan, add the lentils, stock, garlic and thyme. Bring to the boil. Cover and simmer for 15 minutes until tender, adding the green beans for the last 5 minutes of cooking time.
❷ Meanwhile, bring a large pan of water to the boil and cook the pasta according to the packet instructions. Drain and stir into the lentils with the sausage pieces. Heat for 1–2 minutes until piping hot. Remove the sprig of thyme before serving in warmed bowls.

Colcannon with prawns

Colcannon is a hearty Irish potato dish with cabbage and leeks. Here we add prawns to make a very satisfying supper.

5½ POINTS values per recipe • **345** Calories per serving • Takes 30 minutes

200 g (7 oz) potatoes, peeled and cubed
a few leaves of Savoy or other cabbage, shredded
75 ml (3 fl oz) skimmed milk
1 small leek, chopped
low fat cooking spray
1 garlic clove, chopped
100 g (3½ oz) peeled raw prawns
juice of ½ a lemon
1 teaspoon French mustard
salt and freshly ground black pepper

❶ Bring two pans of water to the boil and cook the potatoes and cabbage, separately, for about 15 minutes each, or until soft, and then drain.
❷ Meanwhile, in a small, lidded saucepan, heat the milk with the leek for 5 minutes, covered, until the leek is softened.
❸ Spray a non stick frying pan with the cooking spray and fry the garlic until golden. Add the prawns and stir fry for 2–3 minutes or until pink and cooked through. Pour over the lemon juice and season.
❹ Mash the potatoes with the leeks and milk, and stir in the drained cabbage, mustard and seasoning. Spoon on to a plate and make a little well in the centre. Fill with the prawns and their juices and serve.

Spiced chicken tagine

A warming, sweet and savoury chicken dish that's perfect for a winter's evening home alone. Serve with some steamed zero **POINTS** *value green vegetables, such as* **spinach**, **cabbage** *or* **broccoli**.

6½ **POINTS** values per recipe • **488** Calories per serving • Takes 5 minutes to prepare, 25 minutes to cook

1 x 150 g (5½ oz) skinless boneless chicken breast, cut into bite size pieces
1 onion, chopped
½ teaspoon ground ginger
1 small cinnamon stick
½ teaspoon ground coriander
400 ml (14 fl oz) chicken stock
50 g (1¾ oz) no soak prunes, stoned and chopped
5 olives in brine, stoned and chopped
1 teaspoon runny honey
50 g (1¾ oz) dried couscous
salt and freshly ground black pepper
a handful of chopped fresh coriander, to garnish

❶ Put the chicken in a lidded, non stick saucepan with the onion, ginger, cinnamon stick, coriander, stock and seasoning. Bring to the boil, cover and simmer, stirring occasionally, for 15 minutes.
❷ Add the prunes, olives and honey and cook for a further 5–10 minutes, uncovered, until the sauce is reduced considerably.
❸ Meanwhile, put the couscous in a bowl and pour over enough boiling water to cover it, with 2.5 cm (1 inch) of boiling water above it. Cover the bowl with a plate, foil or tea towel and leave the couscous to steam for at least 5 minutes. Then fluff up with a fork.
❹ Check the seasoning in the tagine and remove the cinnamon stick. Serve the chicken accompanied by the couscous and garnished with coriander.

Cashew and watercress pilau

A satisfying and comforting meal that's also full of the 'good-for-you' factor.

6½ **POINTS** values per recipe • **505** Calories per serving • Takes 20 minutes to prepare, 35 minutes to cook • Ⓥ

low fat cooking spray
3 spring onions, chopped
1 garlic clove, chopped
75 g (2¾ oz) brown basmati rice, washed
¼ cauliflower, chopped into small florets
juice of ½ a lemon
¼ teaspoon Chinese 5 spice powder
100 ml (3½ fl oz) vegetable stock
a small bunch of mint, chopped
a small bunch of parsley, chopped
100 g (3½ oz) watercress, chopped
25 g (1 oz) cashew nuts, toasted and chopped
salt and freshly ground black pepper

❶ Heat a large, lidded saucepan and spray with the cooking spray. Stir fry the spring onions and garlic for a few minutes, adding a splash of water if they start to stick.
❷ Add all the other ingredients except the watercress and cashew nuts and stir together. Cover the pan and simmer for 35 minutes without lifting the lid.
❸ Stir in the watercress and cashew nuts, season and serve.

Szechuan pork

6½ **POINTS** values per recipe • **690** Calories per serving • Takes 30 minutes

2 teaspoons Szechuan peppercorns
¼ teaspoon flaked sea salt
150 g (5½ oz) pork fillet
low fat cooking spray
60 g (2 oz) wide rice noodles
1 pak choi, halved
2 teaspoons shredded fresh root ginger
2 teaspoons Teriyaki sauce

❶ Place the peppercorns in a dry frying pan over a medium heat and heat until toasted and fragrant. Place in a pestle and mortar with the salt and crush together.

❷ Sprinkle the pork with the salt and pepper mixture, patting it into the meat. Heat the frying pan again and spray with the cooking spray. Cook the pork for 4–5 minutes on each side, or until cooked through. Remove the pan from the heat and allow the pork to stand in the pan for 5 minutes.

❸ Bring a pan of water to the boil and cook the rice noodles for 4 minutes and then drain.

❹ Place the pak choi in a steamer (if you don't have a steamer you can use a metal colander over a lidded pan), sprinkle with the ginger and cook for 3–5 minutes, until it is tender.

❺ Serve the pork, sliced, on top of the pak choi and rice noodles. Drizzle with the Teriyaki sauce.

Beef chow mein

Chow mein dishes are a great way to prepare a complete well–balanced meal, all in one pan.

7 POINTS values per recipe • **342** Calories per serving • Takes 15 minutes

60 g (2 oz) medium egg noodles
low fat cooking spray
125 g (4½ oz) lean stir fry beef
4 spring onions, chopped roughly
60 g (2 oz) mange tout
80 g (3 oz) mushrooms, quartered
80 g (3 oz) beansprouts, rinsed
3 tablespoons oyster sauce
juice of a lime (optional)

❶ Bring a pan of water to the boil and cook the noodles for 3 minutes until tender. Drain and rinse in cold water.
❷ Lightly coat a non stick frying pan or wok with the cooking spray. Stir fry the beef and spring onions for 1½ minutes, then add the mange tout and mushrooms and cook for a further 1½ minutes.
❸ Mix in the beansprouts, noodles, oyster sauce and 1 tablespoon of water and heat through for 1–1½ minutes, stirring constantly. Serve immediately, with a little lime juice squeezed over, if using.

Spicy cottage pie

*This slight twist on the standard cottage pie is delicious with steamed or boiled **spring greens**, for no extra **POINTS** values.*

7½ POINTS values per recipe • **414** Calories per serving • Takes 30 minutes • ✱ (for up to 1 month)

low fat cooking spray
½ small onion, diced
1 garlic clove, crushed
125 g (4½ oz) extra lean beef mince
½ teaspoon ground cumin
a pinch of paprika
50 ml (2 fl oz) beef stock
75 ml (3 fl oz) skimmed milk
½ tablespoon tomato purée
½ tablespoon Worcestershire sauce
250 g (9 oz) potatoes, peeled and chopped
1 teaspoon wholegrain mustard
salt and freshly ground black pepper

❶ Heat a large non stick pan and spray with the cooking spray. Fry the onion for 1–2 minutes and then add the garlic and beef mince.
❷ Brown the mince all over, then add the spices. Stir well and then pour in the beef stock, 50 ml (2 fl oz) of the milk, tomato purée and Worcestershire sauce and seasoning. Simmer for 10–15 minutes, stirring occasionally.
❸ Meanwhile, bring a pan of water to the boil and cook the potatoes until tender. Drain and then mash with the remaining milk, wholegrain mustard and seasoning. Preheat the grill.
❹ When all the cooking liquid has evaporated and you have a rich sauce, spoon the meat into an ovenproof dish. Top with the mashed potatoes and place under a hot grill or at the top of a hot oven for 8–10 minutes until golden and bubbling.

Baked lemon turkey rolls

7½ **POINTS** values per recipe • **512** Calories per serving • Takes 10 minutes to prepare, 20 minutes to cook

2 x 75 g (2¾ oz) thin turkey breast steaks
50 g (1¾ oz) reduced fat cottage cheese with
   onion and chives
2 thin slices prosciutto ham
150 ml (5 fl oz) chicken or vegetable stock
1 tablespoon white wine
½ lemon, sliced into wedges
4 garlic cloves, whole
4 cherry tomatoes, halved
60 g (2 oz) tagliatelle
salt and freshly ground black pepper
a handful of basil or parsley, chopped to
   garnish (optional)

❶ Preheat the oven to Gas Mark 4/180°C/fan oven 160°C. Place a piece of clingfilm on the work surface and put the turkey steaks on top. Cover them with another piece of clingfilm and bash gently with a rolling pin or frying pan, to make the steaks bigger and thinner.

❷ Remove the top sheet of clingfilm and spread the cottage cheese on to the steaks. Season.

❸ Roll up the turkey steaks, then roll each in a piece of prosciutto. Place the rolls in a small ovenproof dish.

❹ Pour the stock and wine over the rolls and arrange the lemon, garlic cloves and tomatoes around them. Bake for 20 minutes.

❺ Meanwhile, bring a pan of water to the boil and cook the tagliatelle according to the packet instructions. Drain.

❻ Remove the dish from the oven. Mash the baked garlic and lemon with a fork, removing the papery garlic skins and lemon rind, and stir through the juices. Serve the turkey rolls on top of the tagliatelle and spoon over the juices. Scatter with basil or parsley, if using, and serve.

7 1/2 POINTS VALUE

Index by *POINTS* values

Index